The Minotaur

Retold by
Russell Punter

KU-131-819

Illustrated by Linda Cavallini

Reading consultant: Alison Kelly
Roehampton University

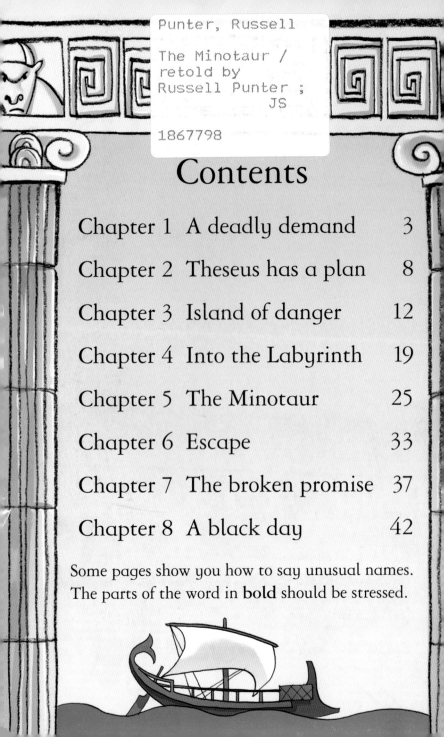

Contents

Some pages show you how to say unusual names.
The parts of the word in **bold** should be stressed.

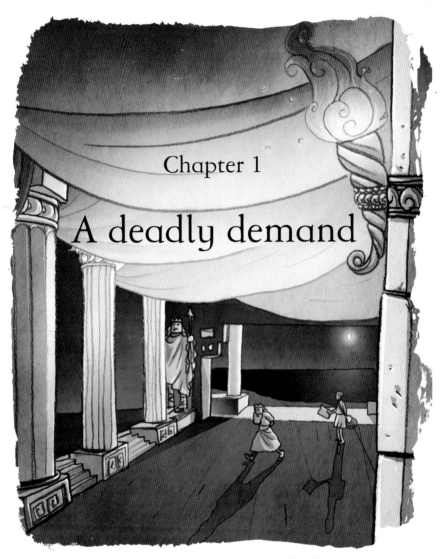

Chapter 1

A deadly demand

Long ago, a king ruled the city of Athens. One day, he received a terrible letter.

"Oh no," he sighed. "Not again. What shall I do?"

"What's wrong?" asked his son, Theseus.

King Aegeus* waved the letter under Theseus's nose. "Read this," he moaned.

*say ee-jee-oos

"Every nine years, King Minos demands fourteen people from Athens," said Aegeus.

"He sends them into a giant maze called the Labyrinth."

"Sounds fun," said Theseus.
"Fun?" spluttered his father.
"At the heart of the Labyrinth
is a Minotaur*."

What's a
Minotaur?

"It's a terrible creature."
Aegeus shivered. "It's half man,
half bull... and it eats people!"

7

*say **my**-no-tore

Chapter 2

Theseus has a plan

"I have an idea," said Theseus.
"I'll be one of the seven men."

"Are you crazy?" said his
father. "The Minotaur will eat
you alive."

"Don't worry, Dad," said
Theseus. "I'm the best sword
fighter in Athens."

Aegeus sighed. "Even if you kill the monster, no one has ever escaped the Labyrinth."

"I'll find a way out somehow," said Theseus confidently.

King Aegeus begged his son not to go. But it was no use.

Theseus boarded a ship with the others. Aegeus was still very worried.

"If Theseus survives," he said to the sailors, "fly white sails on the ship when you return."

11

Chapter 3

Island of danger

Wind filled the ship's sails. Theseus and the others were on their way.

Before they arrived at Crete, Theseus hid his sword under his clothes. Soldiers were waiting for them as they docked.

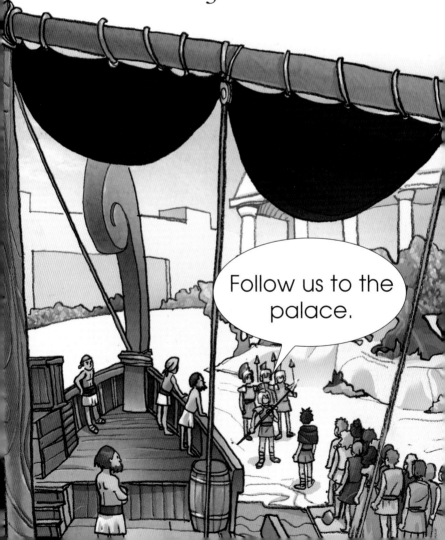

Follow us to the palace.

"Welcome!" roared King Minos. "Enjoy your last meal. At dawn you enter the Labyrinth."

Guards took the prisoners away. They locked them in a dark, dank dungeon.

That night, Ariadne*, the king's daughter, took them bread and water.

As soon as she saw Theseus, Ariadne fell madly in love.

15

*say a-ree-add-nee

"I can't let you spend the rest of your life in the Labyrinth," she whispered.

"Then help me to kill the Minotaur and escape," said Theseus.

Ariadne thought for a
moment. "Very well," she said.
"If you promise to marry me."

"Er, all right," Theseus
agreed nervously.

"Take this ball of magic string," said Ariadne.

"Tie it to the entrance of the Labyrinth, as you go in."

"Then what?" asked Theseus.

"You'll see," smiled Ariadne.

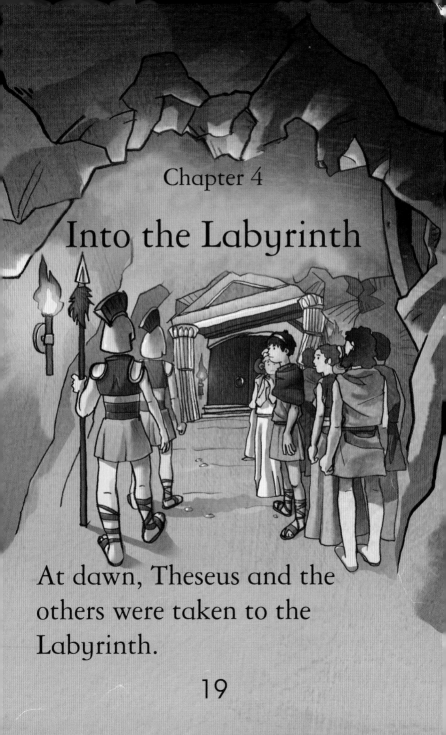

Chapter 4

Into the Labyrinth

At dawn, Theseus and the
others were taken to the
Labyrinth.

When the guards weren't looking, Theseus tied one end of his string to a rock.

"Get inside, all of you!" shouted a guard. One by one, they entered the Labyrinth.

As Theseus went in, the ball
of string jumped from his hand.

Theseus couldn't believe his
eyes. The string rolled along
the ground by itself.

"Which way shall we go?"
said the others.
"Follow me!" said Theseus.

The magical string wound this way and that. Soon they were deep inside the Labyrinth.

The ball of string stopped in a cave.

"Now what?" asked one of the women. *Raaaggghh!*

A terrifying roar echoed around them.

"It's the Minotaur," cried Theseus, "coming this way!"

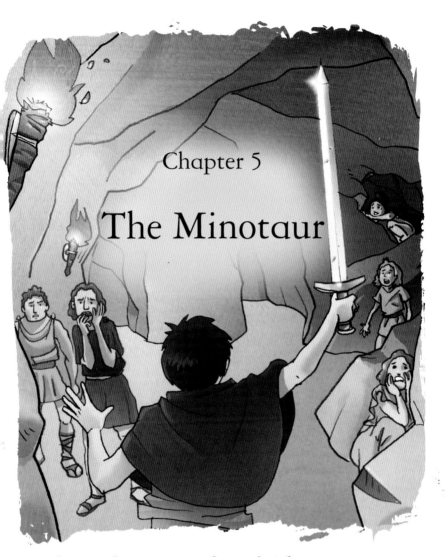

Chapter 5

The Minotaur

The others tried to hide.

"Don't worry," said Theseus, pulling out his sword.

The ground shook. Heavy footsteps came nearer... and nearer. The mighty Minotaur stormed into the cave.

Raaaggghh!

The Minotaur gave a loud snort. Clouds of smelly breath shot from its nostrils.

With an ear-splitting roar, it charged. The young prince swung his sword at the terrifying monster.

The Minotaur was wounded, but it didn't give up. It chased Theseus around the cave.

"Come on, Theseus!" shouted the others. "Don't let it get us."

Theseus tried to fight back, but the monster dodged every blow. Then Theseus tripped.

He looked up to see the Minotaur looming overhead. The hungry creature reached out to grab him.

With one last thrust,
Theseus plunged his sword
into the monster's chest.

The Minotaur gave a
blood-chilling cry, and fell
to the ground with a thud.

31

"Well done, Theseus!" cried the others. "You've saved us."

"It's not over yet," puffed Theseus. "We still have to find a way out."

Chapter 6

Escape

Theseus noticed the magic string lying on the ground. "Perhaps this will help us."

Following the trail of string, Theseus led the others out of the Labyrinth.

Theseus crept up behind the guards at the entrance. Swiftly, he tied them up with the string.

Theseus found Ariadne waiting at the dock. He climbed aboard his ship.

I knew you'd escape.

"Don't forget your promise to marry me," said Ariadne.
"Promise?" said Theseus.
"Oh, er, yes. Come with us."

Chapter 7

The broken promise

On the voyage home, the ship stopped at the island of Naxos.

"We'll spend the night here," said Theseus.

But Theseus couldn't sleep.
He didn't want to marry King
Minos's daughter.

So while Ariadne was asleep,
he woke the others. He ordered
them back to the ship, and
they sailed away.

When Ariadne woke the next
morning, she was heartbroken.
She cried to the gods
for revenge.

A god called Dionysus*
appeared and Ariadne told
him her tale.

Dionysus felt sorry for
Ariadne. "I will punish Theseus
for breaking his promise to
you," he declared.

40

*say die-on-**eye**-sus

Dionysus cast a spell across the sea. "Forget, sailors!" he boomed. "Forget, forget, forget!"

Chapter 8

A black day

Theseus was nearly home. "I can't wait to be back in Athens," he told a sailor.

"Um, me too," said the man, looking up at the black sails.

"What's the matter?" asked Theseus.

"I think I was supposed to do something," replied the sailor. "But I can't remember what."

"That's funny," said another sailor. "I had the same feeling."
"And me," cried a third.

"Oh well," said Theseus, "I'm sure it was nothing important."

Up on the cliffs, King Aegeus looked out to sea. "My son's ship has returned," he cried.

"Oh no, black sails!" he sobbed. "Theseus must be dead."

Aegeus felt terrible. He jumped into the sea and was never seen again.

When Theseus landed, he heard the dreadful news about his father.

Theseus had beaten the Minotaur and escaped from the Labyrinth...

but his father never knew.

About the Minotaur legend

The story of the Minotaur was first told about 3,000 years ago in ancient Greece. Some people think that the noisy Minotaur was invented to explain earthquakes. In 1900, archeologists discovered underground storage passages on Crete. Perhaps they were the inspiration for the Labyrinth?

Usborne Quicklinks

To find out more about ancient Greece, go to the Usborne Quicklinks Website at **www.usborne-quicklinks.com** Read the internet safety guidelines, and then type the keywords "The Minotaur".

Series editor: Lesley Sims

First published in 2009 by Usborne Publishing Ltd., Usborne House, 83-85 Saffron Hill, London EC1N 8RT, England. www.usborne.com
Copyright © 2009 Usborne Publishing Ltd.